Crested Schna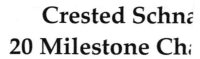
20 Milestone Ch

Crested Schnauzer Memorable Moments. Includes Milestones for Memories, Gifts, Grooming, Socialization & Training

Volume 2

Todays Doggy

Copyright © 2019

Dedicated To All of You Wonderful Owners and Fans

Introduction

Welcome to the Original Doggy Milestone Series™ where you are encouraged to create those special moments with your dog. We have composed the milestones in a way that challenges you to set the stage before taking your photos.

Use props and make it fun - be creative in setting up your photos. Get family and friends involved - take it out with you - use it in different places and settings - have a play with it and most importantly, have a good time!

You can either hold the desired milestone spread open yourself - or have somebody hold it open as you take the snap.

If you would like to have the selected milestone book spread open and standing independently in your photos, you can use one or two large 'foldback' clips to hold the spread open.

Share your photos with friends, family, and communities - look for feedback and areas of improvements in order to create even better memorable photos.

Good luck and enjoy your photo fun.

I

Noticed

You

Were

Sleeping...

So I Helped You Finish The Food

I Look Rather Fetching

...Don't I ?

SORRY...

Too Busy To Talk!

I'M

BBBAD

...Bad
To The
Bone

Today...

Was a "RUFF!" Day

I Have No Idea

What I'm Doing

WHEN YOU'RE HOME ALONE

AND
SOMEONE
KNOCKS
ON THE
DOOR...

MIRROR MIRROR ON THE WALL...

Who's The Doggiest Of Them All?

I'm So GREAT

I Even Know How To High 5

Ahh...

The Joys of Being Groomed

You're Home Early!

I'm Not Lazy

I'm Just On Energy Saving Mode

OH LOOK!

Someone Has Made a Mess!

I Wonder Who Did It!?

As You Can See

I'm
Sleeping

Your Secrets Are Safe With Me

I'm Always Listening

EEEESE

My Dog's Reaction When I Say...

I'm Ready

For My Bedtime Story

I've Got It All...

Under Control

CPSIA information can be obtained
at www.ICGtesting.com
Printed in the USA
LVHW080406210819
628320LV00007B/322/P

Create those memorable moments
with this unique and very challenging
milestone book - the first of it's kind.

Use props in order to set the stage for
each photo. Have family and friends get
involved in the fun.

Share your photos with friends, family
and communities, and enjoy welcoming
feedback.

Good luck with your journey and have a
great time.

Enjoy!

Boweimar

20 Milestone

Challenges

Boweimar Memorable Moments.Includes Milestones for

Memories, Gifts, Socialization & Training

Volume I

NASA Wants To Hire Me — Because I'm a STAR!

NIGHT OUT — With My Doggy Pals

I'm On a SEAFOOD Diet — When I SEE FOOD, I EAT IT!

OFF To The VET?? — CATCH ME IF YOU CAN!

VIP — Very Incredible Pup

I'll Just Be Over Here... — Looking Fabulous

At The Beach! — Having a Wave of a Time

I DIDN'T KNOW WHICH STICK YOU THREW — SO I BOUGHT BACK ALL OF THEM

I Love My Family... — ...And My Family Loves Me